Dominoes

The Real McCoy

and other ghost stories

OXFORD
UNIVERSITY PRESS

OXFORD

UNIVERSITY PRESS

Great Clarendon Street, Oxford OX2 6DP

Oxford University Press is a department of the University of Oxford.
It furthers the University's objective of excellence in research, scholarship,
and education by publishing worldwide in

Oxford New York

Auckland Cape Town Dar es Salaam Hong Kong Karachi
Kuala Lumpur Madrid Melbourne Mexico City Nairobi
New Delhi Shanghai Taipei Toronto

With offices in

Argentina Austria Brazil Chile Czech Republic France Greece
Guatemala Hungary Italy Japan Poland Portugal Singapore
South Korea Switzerland Thailand Turkey Ukraine Vietnam

OXFORD and OXFORD ENGLISH are registered trade marks of
Oxford University Press in the UK and in certain other countries

ISBN: 978 0 19 424451 0

A complete recording of this Dominoes edition of *The Real McCoy and Other Ghost Stories*
is available on cassette ISBN 978 0 19 424444 2

Printed in Hong Kong

ACKNOWLEDGEMENTS

The publisher would like to thank the following for kind permission to reproduce photographs:
Cover (P.Tomkins/VisitScotland/Scottish castle);Alamy pp.7(Mike Danton/Sword,
David Noton Photography/Scottish Castle, Dynamic Graphics/Photis/Key, B.A.E
Inc/Jumping on bed), 19(Stockshot/Alpine scene), 24(Bill Bachman/Australian desert),
25(Danita Delimont/Kangaroo), 38(Philip Lewis/Camp fire, Andrew Holt/Pub,
Peter Titmuss/Bus, Blickwinkel/Fog, Ooteboe/Light blub); Corbis pp.6(Kit Houghton/
Four poster bed), 7(Sandro Vannini/Spiral staircase), 19(Theo Allofs/Zefa/Cracked earth,
Reuters/Earthquake); Getty pp.19(Abode/Kitchen, Peter Dazeley/The Image Bank/
Police officers, Steve Fitchett/Taxi/Sky diving, Henrik Sorensen/Tiled floor);Punchstock
pp.7(Thinkstock/ghost); Robert Harding pp.38(Ken Gillham/camping);

Commissioned photographs by: David Jordan pp. 42, 43; Mark Mason p. 19 (fridge).
Illustrations by: Craig Phillips pp.iv, 1,4,7,10,13,15,17,21,27,33,35,36,37.

Dominoes

SERIES EDITORS: BILL BOWLER AND SUE PARMINTER

The Real McCoy
and other ghost stories

Lesley Thompson

Illustrated by Craig Philips

LEVEL ONE ■ 400 HEADWORDS

Lesley Thompson was born in Newcastle-upon-Tyne, in the North of England, but she moved to Spain some years ago, and now lives near Alicante. She loves reading, the cinema, music, laughing with her friends, and looking at the sea. She also enjoys walking in the countryside in England and Spain, and one day she hopes to walk the *Camino de Santiago* in northern Spain. Lesley has also written *Deep Trouble*, and has adapted *The Secret Agent* in the Dominoes series.

OXFORD
UNIVERSITY PRESS

BEFORE READING

**1 Here are the ghosts in the stories in this book.
Can you match the pictures with the names?**

☐ the ghost of an astronaut

☐ an Australian ghost

☐ the ghost of an animal

☐ a Scottish ghost

☐ a bus-driving ghost

☐ the ghost of a grandfather

2 What do the ghosts in the stories do? Tick three boxes.

a ☐ buy things in a supermarket

b ☐ send messages on a computer

c ☐ throw things onto the floor

d ☐ sit in a garden

e ☐ run after people with a sword

f ☐ drive a plane

1 ⊚ The Real McCoy

'It isn't true!' said Gordon.

Gordon and his friends – Duncan, Fiona and Heather – were in a very old **castle** in the west of Scotland. The castle was now Fiona's **uncle's** hotel. Fiona and her friends were there for the weekend. After dinner, they sat in the **living room** and talked.

'It isn't true,' Gordon said again. 'There isn't a **real ghost** here.'

'There *is* a ghost, Gordon,' said Fiona. 'Look at that picture of Lord McCoy by the door. He died in the bedroom next to the **stairs** and his ghost walks there every night, they say. Nobody sleeps there now.'

They looked up at Lord McCoy. He was in a kilt, or Scottish skirt. His face was white, his eyes were a cold blue, and there was no smile on his thin red mouth. Under Lord McCoy's picture there was a big, old **sword**.

castle a big, old building; a rich person lives here

uncle your father's (or mother's) brother

living room a room where people can sit and talk

real true

ghost a dead person that a living person sees or hears

stairs you can go up or down these in a house

sword a long, sharp knife for fighting

They looked up at Lord McCoy.

'He doesn't look very nice,' said Heather.

'He had three wives and they all died young,' said Fiona. 'Perhaps he killed them!'

'Look at his eyes,' said Duncan. 'They look angry.'

'He's an old man in a picture, that's all,' said Gordon. 'The ghost is a **stupid** story for visitors. It makes the hotel more interesting.'

'OK, Gordon. So why don't you sleep in Lord McCoy's bedroom tonight?' Duncan laughed.

'That's a good **idea**! Do it, Gordon!' said Fiona.

'Are you **scared**, Gordon?' asked Heather.

'No, I'm not,' Gordon answered. 'I'm going to do it! I'm going to sleep in Lord McCoy's bedroom. It's nearly eleven o'clock. Let's go upstairs now!'

The four friends went up the stairs. Gordon opened the door of Lord McCoy's room and they all looked in. The only things in the dark room were a big, old bed and two chairs.

Gordon went into the room and sat down on the bed.

'It's a nice bed. I can sleep very well here. Goodnight, everybody! See you in the morning!' he said.

Duncan, Fiona and Heather said goodnight, closed the bedroom door, and went downstairs again.

'Gordon *is* going to see a ghost tonight!' said Duncan when they were back in the living room.

'What? But there isn't really a ghost,' said Heather. 'The Lord McCoy story isn't true, you know.'

'I know! Gordon's going to see *me*!' said Duncan. 'I'm going to be Lord McCoy. I'm going to wait for two hours. Then I'm going to go to McCoy's room and have a laugh!'

'Oh, yes! I want to see this!' laughed Fiona.

'Me too!' said Heather. '**Wake** us **up** at one o'clock,

Duncan. We want to go with you!'

Soon after that the three friends went to bed.

Gordon was on the bed in Lord McCoy's room. The room was cold and the big, old bed wasn't very nice. It was very dark. The rain hit the window. Gordon remembered the face of Lord McCoy in the picture. After half an hour, Gordon's eyes closed and he slept.

But in his sleep, Gordon saw Lord McCoy once more. He came **towards** Gordon and he laughed. He had a big sword in his hand. Gordon was scared. He wanted to run but he couldn't move. Gordon could see McCoy's white face. It came nearer and nearer. McCoy's sword was over his head now. Gordon wanted to **scream**. He opened his mouth but he couldn't speak.

Suddenly Gordon woke up. His mouth was open and he felt very thirsty. He felt scared, too. Then he laughed. It was only a **dream**. He must forget the stupid stories about old McCoy.

The room felt colder than before. Suddenly, he heard a noise. What was it? Gordon listened carefully. He sat up. It was dark and he could see nothing. But there was a noise. He waited and listened. The noise wasn't there now. He closed his eyes again and slept.

This time, his dream was different. There were three young women in it. One of the women looked at something behind Gordon, screamed and began to run away. Then someone behind him laughed. Was it Lord McCoy's laugh? Gordon woke up suddenly.

Just then, he heard a new noise. This time it came from the door. Gordon sat up and looked towards it. He could see

towards nearer

scream to give a loud, high cry because you are afraid

dream pictures that you see in your head when you are sleeping

3

Gordon listened and didn't move.

nothing, but he could hear the big old **key** in the door. Gordon listened and didn't move.

'Oh no! Someone's **locking** the door!' he thought.

Now something moved at Gordon's feet. There was something on the bed! Gordon was very, very scared by now. The thing on the bed began to move slowly towards him. First it was on his feet and then it moved onto his legs . . .

key you can close or open a door with this

lock to close with a key

jump to move fast on your legs from one thing to a different thing

Gordon **jumped** out of bed and ran towards the door. Behind him, someone laughed. Quickly, his hand found the key and he opened the door. He ran out of the room. There was someone behind him! He saw the sword over his head. He jumped down all the stairs to the door of the living room. Someone was behind him. He looked back

4

slowly. It was Duncan.

'Are you all right, Gordon?'

'Duncan! It was *you*! Yes, I'm OK now. How did you do that thing with the key? That was very good!'

Just then, Fiona and Heather arrived.

'What a noise!' said Heather. 'Gordon! What are you doing here? You didn't wake us up, Duncan! We didn't see you go into McCoy's room!'

Duncan looked at the girls. His face was white.

'It wasn't me. I didn't wake up at one o'clock. But later I heard a lot of noise downstairs, so I came down.'

'What?' said Gordon. 'But it was you, Duncan. You came into my bedroom.'

'No, I didn't,' said Duncan.

'You locked the door, and ran after me with a sword.'

'What sword?' asked Duncan. 'What are you talking about?'

'Lord McCoy's sword! Look up there, under the picture!'

They all looked under the picture of Lord McCoy. But there was no sword there now.

'There's nothing there,' said Fiona.

'Look at the picture,' said Heather. 'That sword wasn't there before!'

They looked at the picture. On the right, next to the old man there was a table, and on it there was a big sword.

'Yes, that's it,' said Gordon slowly.

The four friends looked at the picture without speaking. Lord McCoy looked back at them. There was a smile on his white face now – a very cold, dark smile.

'So the ghost in my room was "**the real McCoy**" after all!' said Gordon.

the real McCoy
a phrase that means 'the real thing'

READING CHECK

Are these sentences true or false? Tick the boxes.

		True	False
a	Fiona and her friends are at her uncle's hotel.	☐	☑
b	Her uncle is Lord McCoy.	☐	☐
c	Gordon sleeps in Lord McCoy's bedroom.	☐	☐
d	Gordon sleeps very well.	☐	☐
e	Duncan wants to visit Gordon in Lord McCoy's bedroom.	☐	☐
f	Duncan runs after Gordon with a sword.	☐	☐
g	Lord McCoy's picture changes after his visit to Gordon.	☐	☐
h	Gordon does not laugh at ghosts now.	☐	☐

WORD WORK

1 Complete the sentences with the pairs of words in the bed.

scream/dream
idea/stupid
woke up/locking
living room/uncle
scared/towards

a Fiona's ..uncle... had a castle with a big .living room .

b 'The .... of ghosts is ....,' said Gordon.

c When the ghost came .... him he felt very ....

d When he had the bad ...., he wanted to ....

e Suddenly he................... 'Someone's .... the door!' he thought.

2 Match the words with the pictures.

> castle ~~ghost~~ jump key stairs sword

a .ghost

b ....

c ....

d ....

e ....

f ....

GUESS WHAT

The next story, 'Strange Messages', is about a girl called Anna. What happens in it?
Complete the sentences.

a Anna is a good *detective* *student* *doctor* .

b Julia is Anna's *teacher* *sister* *best friend* .

c Anna gets a computer from *her uncle* *her mother* *her father* .

d Anna's ghost is *bad* *nice* *ill* .

e At the end of the story Anna is *happy* *famous* *afraid* .

2 ◉ Strange Messages

Anna was at her best friend Julia's house. She often went there to do **homework** with her. It was their last year of **school**, and they always had a lot of homework.

'Anna, what are you going to do when you leave school?' asked Julia. 'Are you going to go to **college**?'

'Perhaps. I don't really know,' said Anna.

Anna didn't want to tell Julia, but she had a wonderful **ambition**: she wanted to go up into **space**.

'One day,' she thought, 'I'm going to be an **astronaut**.'

Anna wrote a letter to **NASA** in America. She wanted to work there. She said nothing to her mother and father about it. They didn't understand.

'Anna's going to be a doctor,' her mother said to all their friends. When she heard that, Anna smiled. She didn't want to be a doctor. She had different ideas.

One day, Anna's Uncle Bob came to her house. Anna liked Uncle Bob. He was different from her mother and father. He knew about Anna's ambition.

'Hello, Anna. Would you like this old computer? I have a new one now. You can do your homework on it.'

'Oh, yes. Thank you, Uncle Bob.'

Anna put the computer in her bedroom. That night, she went to bed and dreamt about going into space. At two o'clock in the morning she suddenly woke up. The computer was **on**.

'That's **strange**,' she thought, but she soon went back to sleep.

homework when you learn at home, usually in the evening or at the weekend

school students learn here

college you study here after you leave school

ambition a big thing that you want to do (before you die)

space the sun and stars are in this

astronaut this person works in space

NASA National Aeronautics and Space Administration (USA); people learn to be astronauts here

on working

strange not usual

'Be careful!' called Mum.

The lights went out again, and there were more strange noises. We were all very scared by now.

'Follow Dad!' Mum screamed. So we all ran out into the garden. Just then, the **ground** began to move under our feet. Then there was a very big noise.

'It's an **earthquake**!' screamed Dad.

The ground moved again and again. We stopped running and looked back at our house. It suddenly **fell** to the ground in front of our eyes.

After the earthquake finished, we all stood quietly for some minutes. Then Gran spoke.

'Well, we lost our house, but we're all alive! It was George. He helped us.' she said quietly. 'He took us out of the house. Look, there are his footprints in the snow.'

We all looked down at the ground. It was dark, but we could see some footprints in the snow. They were the footprints of very big feet.

'Thank you, Grandad,' I said quietly. 'Thank you for helping us.'

ground we walk on this

earthquake when the ground moves suddenly

fall (*past* **fell**) to go down quickly

We could see some footprints in the snow.

READING CHECK

Correct the sentences.

a The family live in a house in ~~Australia.~~ New Zealand

b Grandad George had very big hands.

c When winter comes, there is a lot of rain.

d The ghost goes into the kitchen and closes all the doors.

e The ghost puts Sally's computer on the floor.

f Dad walks after the ghost into the garden.

g The family lose their car in the earthquake.

h The ghost is Sally's brother.

WORD WORK

1 Find eight words from the story in the footprint.

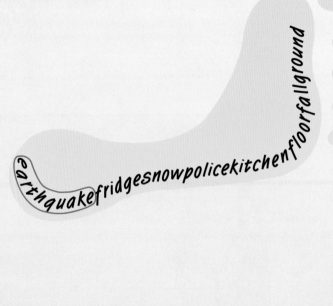

earthquakefridgesnowpolicekitchenfloorfallground

2 Match the words in Activity 1 with the pictures.

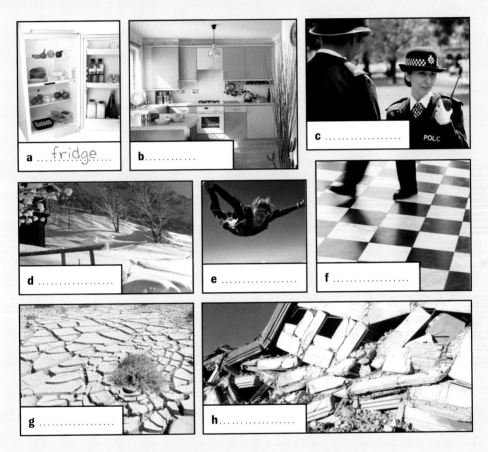

a ...fridge.....

b ....

c ....

d ....

e ....

f ....

g ....

h ....

GUESS WHAT

**The next story, 'A Christmas Ghost', happens in Australia.
What are you going to read about? Tick three boxes.**

a ☐ A cold winter's day.

b ☐ A big Christmas dinner.

c ☐ A young ghost.

d ☐ Driving across Australia.

e ☐ Seeing a strange animal.

f ☐ Listening to Christmas songs.

4 ✪ A Christmas Ghost

'It's nearly Christmas! Where's the snow?' asked Alex.

'Alex!' laughed Dan. 'We're in Australia. They don't have snow here at Christmas.'

Dan and Alex were from London. They worked in a big office, but at Christmas the office was closed for two weeks. This year they wanted to do something different for Christmas, so they were here in Australia.

When they arrived, they got a car at the airport and drove for **miles** across the country towards Alice Springs. In the evenings they stopped at small hotels. There were no cars on the roads, and they saw no houses or people in the country. It was very hot.

'This is going to be a strange Christmas for us,' said Alex. 'No snow, no Christmas tree . . .'

'Oh, be quiet, Alex! We're going to have a wonderful time. It's going to be different, that's all,' said Dan.

It was their third day. They left their hotel early that morning but the sun was soon hot. Suddenly Dan called out, 'Look, Alex! A **kangaroo**!'

The strange animal jumped across the road and disappeared. Then everything was quiet again. They drove for two hours. Then they stopped and ate some sandwiches and drank some water.

'OK, come on, Alex. Let's go,' said Dan. 'We're nearly there. We're going to be in Alice Springs tonight.'

But when Dan **turned** the key, nothing happened. The car didn't move.

'What's the matter, Dan? Is the car OK?

'I don't know. Let's look at the **engine**.'

mile 1.6 kilometres

kangaroo this Australian animal jumps with its strong back legs and long tail

turn to move round

engine the machine in a car that makes it move

They got out and looked at the engine.

'Everything looks OK to me,' said Dan. 'I don't understand.'

'What are we going to do?' asked Alex. 'We're miles from the next town and there aren't any cars on this road. We need some help.'

They waited for nearly four hours. The sun was much hotter now. Alex and Dan sat on the road next to the car. They were scared. They didn't have much to eat and they didn't have much water. They needed help . . . soon!

Dan was asleep.

'Wake up, Dan. Somebody's coming!' called Alex.

It was true. A car **appeared** on the road and came towards them. Dan jumped up with Alex.

'Stop! Stop!' they cried.

The car stopped, and a young man got out. He was about nineteen years old, tall, and he had long brown hair.

'Hello,' he said. 'Do you need help with your car?'

appear to be suddenly in front of someone's eyes

The car stopped, and a young man got out.

'Yes, please! Do you know about engines?'

The young man looked at the engine.

'Ah, yes. You need a **garage**. There's one in the next town. I can take you there.'

Dan and Alex got into the back of the young man's car.

'Were you there for a long time?' he asked.

'About four hours. We were very happy to see you! We didn't have much water,' said Dan.

'Only four hours? I was by the road once and I waited for help for ten days . . .' said the young man.

'For ten days? Is that true?' cried Dan. 'What happened?'

'Oh, it's a long story and I need to watch the road. There are lots of kangaroos around here, you know.'

The young man drove carefully, and Dan and Alex slept in the back. It was about fifty miles to the next town, and when they arrived it was dark. The young man stopped near the garage, but he didn't get out of the car.

'Here you are,' he said. 'Goodbye – Happy Christmas!'

'Thanks again,' said Dan and Alex. 'Goodbye!'

The car soon **disappeared**.

The man in the garage talked to Dan. 'It's late now, but I can go with you tomorrow to your car. Tonight, you can stay in the hotel.'

Dan and Alex went to the small hotel. They asked the woman there for a room. She gave them a key, but she didn't smile. She had a very sad face.

They went to their room.

'The people here aren't very happy,' said Alex. 'It's nearly Christmas, but nobody's getting ready for it.'

garage you buy things here for your car

disappear to go away suddenly

'Yes, it's strange,' said Dan. 'But that young man with the car was nice. And the man at the garage is going to help us. Tomorrow we can go to Alice Springs.'

That night Dan and Alex woke up three times. Every time they heard a strange noise.

'Someone's crying, I think,' said Alex.

The next day, they got up early and went to the garage. The man drove them to their car and looked at the engine. He worked on it for about an hour, and soon Dan and Alex were on the road again. Late that night, they arrived in Alice Springs. This time, their hotel was much nicer.

'Let's go out for something to eat,' said Dan excitedly.

'Wait a minute,' said Alex. 'What's that on the TV?'

Dan turned and looked at the TV.

'Last night, somebody found the body of John Sharp. It was by the road, fifty miles from Little Creek. John disappeared a year ago. At that time, the police found his car, but they never found his body. John was nineteen and he lived in Little Creek. His parents have a hotel there . . .'

A picture of the hotel appeared on the TV.

'Dan,' said Alex quietly, 'that was our hotel in Little Creek. We stayed there last night.'

Just then, the photograph of a young man appeared on the TV. He had long brown hair.

'It's him!' cried Dan. 'It's the young man. He helped us!'

'But he's dead. How could he help us? I don't understand.'

Dan said nothing. Alex looked at him.

'What are you thinking, Dan?'

'We saw a ghost,' said Dan. 'A nice Christmas ghost.'

READING CHECK

1 Match the first and second parts of these sentences.

a Dan and Alex are driving across . . .

b They want to go . . .

c Their car stops . . .

d A young man . . .

e The people in the small hotel . . .

f Dan and Alex see . . .

g The young man is dead . . .

h John Sharp . . .

1 they learn.

2 are very sad.

3 the country in Australia.

4 to Alice Springs.

5 was the name of the ghost.

6 takes them to the next town.

7 the young man on TV.

8 miles from the next town.

2 Correct the mistakes in these sentences.

a Dan and Alex work in a big ~~school~~ *office* in London.

b They are going across Australia by train.

c John Sharp waited for help for two days.

d When the young man leaves Dan and Alex, he says 'Happy Birthday!'

e At night in the small hotel, someone is laughing.

f The hotel in Alice Springs is worse than the hotel in Little Creek.

g Somebody found John Sharp's dog last night.

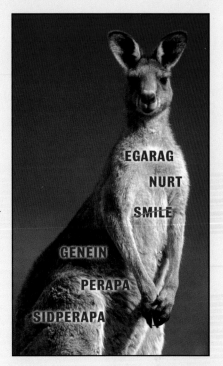

WORD WORK

1 **Find words from the story in the kangaroo.**

2 **Use the words from Activity 1 in the correct form to complete these sentences.**

a I can walk two …miles…… in thirty minutes.

b Is your car in the ……………… or in the street?

c The ……………… in this car isn't very good.

d The girl ……………… last week. The police are looking for her.

e When Dan ……………… the key, nothing happened.

f A young man suddenly ……………… on the road and walked towards them.

EGARAG
NURT
SMILE
GENEIN
PERAPA
SIDPERAPA

GUESS WHAT

The next story is 'The Egyptian Cat'. What are you going to read about? Tick three boxes.

a ☐ a man selling cats in Egypt

b ☐ a French detective

c ☐ shopping

d ☐ a young Egyptian woman

e ☐ an English woman and her husband

f ☐ a ghost in a taxi

5 ◉ The Egyptian Cat

Jill was on holiday in Cairo with Alan, her husband. Alan was a teacher and he wanted to teach his students all about **Ancient** Egypt. So Alan and Jill visited the **Pyramids**, and the Egyptian **Museum**.

'Let's go to the **market** today,' said Alan at breakfast on their last day.

'Good idea,' said Jill. 'I love shopping!'

Later that morning, Alan and Jill walked through the market. There were lots of little shops there.

In one of the shops Alan bought some Egyptian pictures, and in the next shop Jill saw a little white **wooden** dog and a black wooden cat. Jill liked cats.

'Look at this interesting cat, Alan. I'm going to **buy** it.'

The man in the shop spoke to Jill.

'That's a very old cat,' he said. 'Be very careful with it.'

Jill bought the cat and she and Alan left the shop.

The man called after her, 'Be very careful with that cat! It's **magic**!'

Jill laughed. 'It isn't really magic. He says that to everybody when they leave his shop.

When they got back to England, Jill put the black cat on the table in the living room. Now she had six cats from six different countries on that table.

But, a week later, Jill began to find the black Egyptian cat in different **places** in the house. One day it was on the chair in the living room. The next day it was on the floor. Then she found it in the kitchen.

ancient very old

Pyramids very old and famous Egyptian buildings

museum a building where people go to look at old things

market where people go to buy things in the street

wooden made of wood

buy (*past* **bought**) to give someone money for something

magic unusual and making things happen in a way that you can't understand

place where something is

She told Alan about it that weekend.

'What? Is that Egyptian cat moving?' Alan laughed. 'That man was right. Perhaps it is a magic cat after all! Cats were very important in Ancient Egypt, you know.'

'Don't laugh, Alan,' said Jill. 'I don't like it.'

One evening, Jill came home from work and found the wooden cat in the garden.

'Alan, did you put the Egyptian cat in the garden?' asked Jill when Alan came home.

'Of course not!' said Alan. 'Is it moving again? Perhaps you need to put it away in a box.'

Jill began to feel afraid of the Egyptian cat. So she did put it away in a box in the bedroom.

That night Jill slept badly. The Egyptian cat appeared in her dreams. Its eyes were yellow and angry.

'What do you want?' Jill asked. But the cat did not answer.

The next morning Jill woke up and saw the cat. It was on the floor next to her bed.

She felt scared. 'I can't tell Alan,' she thought. 'It's stupid to be afraid of a wooden cat.'

'Be very careful with it.'

After breakfast, Jill walked to work. She took the Egyptian cat with her. In the street she saw a **litter bin**, and she put the cat in it.

'Don't come back!' she said, and she walked away quickly.

When Jill came home that evening, she couldn't see the cat in the house.

'No cat – good!' she thought.

Suddenly she heard the telephone. She answered it at once. Someone from the hospital spoke to her.

'Your husband had an accident,' they said. 'His car went off the road and into a river. He nearly died! He's alive, but he isn't very well.'

Jill went to the hospital at once. She saw Alan in his bed there, but he couldn't speak. She went home and began to cry.

'That cat! That cat did it. It was angry with me. I wasn't careful with it. I put it in the litter bin and Alan nearly died! What am I going to do?'

Quickly, Jill went out into the street to find the cat. But there were lots of litter bins in the street. Which was the right bin? Jill couldn't remember, so she looked in all of them. She was there for a long time. It was ten o'clock at night and very dark when Jill suddenly said: 'Here it is!'

She carefully put the little black Egyptian cat in her bag, and took it home. She put it back on the table in the living room with the five cats from five different countries.

litter bin a box in the street where you put things that you don't want or need

The next day, Alan came home from hospital. He began to feel better.

Jill didn't tell Alan about the Egyptian cat, but at the weekend she took it to a museum in London. The man there looked at it for a very long time.

'This cat is very, very old,' he said. 'It's an Ancient Egyptian cat. Cats were very important to the Ancient Egyptians. Where did you get it?'

Jill told the man in the museum about the market in Cairo and about the old man in the shop there. She told him about the times when she found the cat in different places in the house, about the time when she put it in the litter bin, and about Alan's car accident.

The man didn't smile or laugh at her.

'Perhaps someone took this cat from an ancient **tomb**,' he told Jill. 'In the past, bad men often took things from Ancient Egyptian tombs. And when you take something from a tomb, bad things happen to you, many Egyptians believe.'

'I see,' said Jill. 'Now I understand. But what can I do?'

'The cat must go back home to Egypt,' said the man. 'You can give it to the Egyptian museum in Cairo.'

So the next week, Jill put the wooden cat in a little box and **sent** it to the Egyptian museum in Cairo. Alan soon got well again after that, and Jill was happy once more with the five cats on her living room table – and she never bought a cat from a different country again!

tomb where people put a dead person

send (*past* **sent**) to leave something for a postman to take

READING CHECK

Correct nine more mistakes in the summary of this story.

      teacher

Jill and Alan, a ~~student~~, go to Egypt on holiday. Jill buys a little brown wooden cat in a

shop. Jill takes the cat to England and puts it with all her cats from different countries.

One day, she finds the Egyptian cat out of the house in the street. She feels afraid of the

cat. She puts it in a bag in the bedroom. The next day, Jill tries to lose the cat. Later,

someone phones Jill. Alan is in school and he isn't very well. Jill finds the cat again and

takes it to Paris. She tells the man there about the old woman in the shop in Cairo.

The man laughs at her. The next week, the cat goes back home to London. Now Jill has five

cats and she is sad once more.

WORD WORK

1 Complete the sentences with the words inside the pyramids.

a When we went to Egypt, we saw a lot of old t o m b s .

m
b   o
s   t

b Jill bought the little wooden cat at an Egyptian __ __ __ __ __ __ .

a
k   e
r   m   t

c The __ __ __ __ __ __ __ in Cairo has some interesting things to see.

e
u   m
s   u   m

d The Pyramids are very __ __ __ __ __ __ __ __ buildings.

a
e   n
c
n   t   i

e Please put that paper in the __ __ __ __ __ __   __ __ __!

f Egypt is an interesting __ __ __ __ __ __.

g That wooden cat can move. It's __ __ __ __ __ __!

h Jill wants to __ __ __ __ __ the cat back to Egypt.

GUESS WHAT

The next story is 'The Last Bus'. Who are you going to read about? Tick three boxes.

a ☐ a strange woman

b ☐ a photographer

c ☐ a bus driver

d ☐ a teacher

e ☐ a student

f ☐ three friends

6 ☉ The Last Bus

Steve, Nick, and Tom were in the Yorkshire hills. They liked **camping** and they liked going to different **campsites** at the weekend.

'I love camping,' said Steve.

The friends sat on the ground by their **fire** in the campsite and talked.

'I love camping, too, but it's very cold tonight,' said Nick. 'Let's find a warm **pub** and go and sit in it and have a drink or two.'

'A pub?' said Tom. 'A good idea! But did you see one near here?'

'Oh, we went past a pub when we came here,' said Nick. 'It's about two miles down the road. Let's go.'

There were no cars on the road, and after a long walk they arrived at the pub. They could see the **lights** in the pub through the windows.

'Not many people in there tonight,' said Tom. 'And it's Friday. Where is everybody?'

They went into the pub, got some drinks, and sat down near the fire. A young woman sat by the window. She had very long black hair, but they couldn't see her face. She looked out of the window.

'What's that woman looking at?' Steve asked. 'It's very dark out there.'

'Perhaps she's waiting for someone,' said Nick.

'She's waiting for the last **bus**,' said a man in the pub. He was a little old man and he sat down at the table next to them.

'The last bus? I see. Does it go to the campsite?' asked Tom.

camp to stay and sleep somewhere in the open country

campsite you can camp here

fire this is red, and hot, and it burns

pub a building where people go to have a drink

light a thing that helps you to see in the dark

bus a big car that lots of people use to go from one place to another

'Oh, yes. It does,' the man laughed. 'It leaves when the pub closes.'

'It leaves when the pub closes.'

The friends drank and talked. When the pub closed, the woman with long black hair got up and walked out into the night.

'She's going to get the last bus,' said Tom. 'Let's follow her.'

Just then, an old bus appeared very suddenly on the road and stopped outside the pub. The bus door opened and the woman got on.

'Good evening, Rose,' said the bus driver.

'Good evening to you,' said the woman to the driver. 'These three young men behind me are going to the campsite.'

'Are they now? The campsite? OK. Get on!' said the driver to the three friends.

'And remember, driver,' said Rose, 'You must drive carefully tonight!' And she laughed, but it was a very strange laugh, long and slow.

'Of course, Rose,' the driver said. 'I always drive carefully.'

The three friends felt scared, but they didn't want to walk back to the campsite, so they got on the bus.

It was very dark in the bus, and they couldn't see very well. They couldn't see the driver's face, but they could see his hands. They were very white. Then the bus door closed, and the driver began to drive his old bus along the country road back to the campsite – very fast!

Suddenly, the bus stopped. Some strange people appeared and got on. They were people from perhaps seventy years ago. They wore strange coats and hats. They didn't speak, but the driver talked to them. He also laughed a lot, and drove faster and faster. Then the bus stopped near a river, and all the strange people got off.

'Where are they going?' asked Steve. 'There aren't any houses here!'

The people disappeared quickly into the dark night. Now there was a lot of **fog** on the road. The three friends could see nothing at all through the window. They were truly scared.

'How can he drive in this fog?' asked Nick. 'He can't see a thing!'

fog bad weather that makes it difficult to see

The driver laughed and drove faster. they could hear nothing – only the noise of the engine.

'He's going to kill us!' said Steve. Now they felt very scared.

'Please drive more slowly,' screamed Tom. The driver didn't answer.

Steve stood up, but the bus moved suddenly, and he fell on the floor.

'Ow!' he said. 'That stupid driver. What's the matter with him?'

Suddenly, the bus stopped again and the door opened. The three friends ran to the door and jumped off. Without saying anything, the driver closed the door and drove away. The bus disappeared in the fog.

The driver laughed and drove faster.

'Phew!' said Tom. 'What a bad driver! Where are we now?'

'Near the campsite,' said Nick. 'Look! It's up the hill over there.'

The friends walked back towards the campsite. Someone sat near their fire.

'Look!' said Steve. 'It's the woman from the pub. She's sitting by our fire.'

'How did she get there before us?' asked Nick. 'I don't understand. Let's go and talk to her. Perhaps she knows something about that strange bus!'

But when they got to the fire, the woman wasn't there any more. The three friends felt scared. That night they couldn't sleep.

'Who was she?' they all thought.

In the morning, they asked the man at the campsite about the strange woman and the old bus.

'It's the woman from the pub.'

'Oh, yes. That was Rose,' he said. 'She stayed here

perhaps seventy years ago with her husband. One night, he went to the pub and took the last bus back to the campsite. But there was an accident, and all the people on the bus died. After this, Rose was very sad and she died young a year later. She comes here sometimes, people say, and waits for her husband . . .'

When the friends heard this, they left the campsite very quickly and ran to the nearest town. They found a different pub there, and sat down and had a drink.

'That man at the campsite – did you see his hands? They were very white . . .' said Steve.

'And he had a strange laugh . . .' said Tom.

'Yes,' said Nick. '*He* was the bus driver!'

'The next time we go to a new place, let's stay in a hotel!' said Steve.

READING CHECK

What do they say?

1 I always drive carefully.

2 I love camping, too, but it's very cold tonight.

3 Please drive more slowly.

4 She's waiting for the last bus.

5 That was Rose. She stayed here perhaps seventy years ago with her husband.

6 The last bus? Does it go to the campsite?

7 The next time we go to a new place, I'd like to stay in a hotel!

8 You must drive carefully tonight!

a Nick says to his friends, '..2..'
b A man in the pub says to the three friends, '......'
c Tom asks the man in the pub, '......'
d Rose says to the bus driver, '......'
e The bus driver says to Rose, '......'
f Tom screams to the bus driver, '......'
g The man at the campsite says to the three friends, '......'
h Steve says to his friends, '......'

WORD WORK

1 Match the words with the pictures.

bus ~~campsite~~ fire fog light pub

a campsite

b ....

c ....

d ....

e ....

f ....

2 Complete the story with the words from Activity 1.

Last weekend, I went to a a) ...campsite... with some friends. It was cold so we walked to the b) .... in the next village for a drink. There was a nice big c) .... in the room and we had a good evening. When we left the pub, it was dark and there was a lot of d) .... Then we saw a white e) ....
and we heard a noise. But it was only a f) ...., and the driver took us back to the campsite in a few minutes.

WHAT NEXT?

Here are two more stories with ghosts in them.
Which would you like to read next? Why?

THE CURSE OF THE MUMMY

The ghost of Tutankhamun appears in the dreams of Tariq, a young Egyptian boy in the 1920s, when he is working with Howard Carter to find Tutankhamun's tomb. Over time Tariq dreams more, and his dreams get stranger. What do they mean, and what must Howard Carter do with Tutankhamun's body when he finds it?

✚ Macbeth ✚

The ghost of Macbeth's best friend Banquo appears to him one night at dinner. There are many people in the room, but Macbeth is the only one to see the ghost. Banquo says nothing, but Macbeth is afraid. Why is this? And can Banquo stop his friend from following the dark and strange ambitions of his wife, Lady Macbeth?

PROJECT A Emails

1 Read this email from Gordon to his friend Beth. Finish the sentences below.

⬜ ❌ ⬜

Hi Beth,

I went to Scotland at the weekend. Fiona's uncle has a hotel near Oban. I slept in room number 13 there – a ghost's bedroom! The ghost's name is Lord McCoy and he lived about 350 years ago. I had bad dreams in the night. McCoy was in them – with his sword. I woke up. Then I heard a noise. The key turned in the door, but there was nobody there! Then there was something on the bed. I got up and ran! I saw a sword over my head. I fell down the stairs onto the wooden living room floor. Duncan was behind me. I was very angry with him and said, 'Why did you do that?' He said, 'It wasn't me, Gordon. I was in bed.'

I looked at the picture of McCoy on the wall over the fireplace. There was a sword next to him in the picture! It wasn't there before – it was on the wall.

What do you think, Beth? Did I see a ghost?

a Gordon stayed at a hotel near .... in Scotland.

b He stayed in Lord McCoy's bedroom – room number ....

c Lord McCoy lived .... years ago.

d Gordon dreamed of McCoy, and his ....

e He ran from the room and fell downstairs onto the .... living room floor.

f Gordon was .... with Duncan.

g McCoy's picture over the .... was different. There was a sword in it.

2 Read Beth's conversation in a chat room with Gordon.
Match the answers in the box below with the questions.

Beth: Hi Gordon. I've got some questions for you.

Gordon: OK. Ask me.

Beth: Who was at the hotel with you?

Gordon: a) My friends, Fiona, Heather, and Duncan

Beth: Where was Fiona's uncle?

Gordon: b) ....

Beth: Is Duncan a good friend?

Gordon: c) ....

Beth: When did Lord McCoy die?

Gordon: d) ....

Beth: How did he die?

Gordon: e) ....

Beth: Was he married?

Gordon: f) ....

Beth: Are there animals in the house?

Gordon: g) ....

Beth: Is there more than one picture of Lord McCoy?

Gordon: h) ....

Beth: Did you drink anything before you went to bed?

Gordon: i) ....

Beth: Did your friends see the ghost, too?

Gordon: j) ....

About 350 years ago.	No, they didn't.
He fell off his horse.	Perhaps, but I only know this one.
He was away on holiday.	There are some dogs.
I had a glass of milk.	Yes, he is.
~~My friends, Fiona, Heather, and Duncan.~~	Yes, three times.

3 Do you think the ghost was, or wasn't real? Write an email from Beth to Gordon
with your ideas.

PROJECT B Looking for ghosts

**1 Do you want to look for ghosts? Then you need these things.
Match the words with the pictures. Use a dictionary to help you.**

[4] a torch
[ ] a camera
[ ] some flour
[ ] a thermometer
[ ] a coin, some paper
[ ] a notebook and pencil

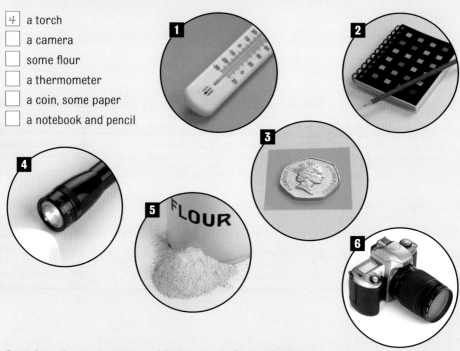

2 Complete these sentences with the words from Activity 1.

a You need ..a..thermometer.. . This tells you when it is hot or cold.
(Ghosts usually make the room cold.)

b You can write down anything strange or exciting that happens with ....

c Put .... on .... on the floor. Draw round it with your
pencil. Real ghosts don't move things when they walk.

d Ghosts usually like dark places. You can see better with ....

e Put .... on the floor and on tables and chairs. Real ghosts don't leave
handprints and footprints.

f Use .... to take photos of the ghost. Sometimes we can see things better in
photos.

3 Here are more things. What can you use these for?

a Matches   see / with / when / torch / breaks

....

....

b A bag   carry / things / in

....

....

c A mobile phone   phone / for help / with

....

....

d A video camera   film / ghost / with

....

....

e A watch   see / the time / with

....

....

f A tape recorder   record / noises / with

....

....

4 Imagine you went looking for ghosts last night. Complete this table.

Which friend did you go with?	
Where did you go?	
What did you take?	
Why?	
What did you see and hear?	
How did you feel?	
Where did you run?	
What did you tell your friends?	
What did they say?	
What are you going to do tomorrow?	

5 Complete the story with the information in the table.

I went with my friend .... We went to

....

We took .... and

.... with us to .... ,

and we took ....

and .... to ....

At first, nothing happened. Then we heard ....
The room suddenly went cold.

We saw ....

We felt ....

We ran ....

We told our friends. They ....

Tomorrow ....